A road for my car

By Debbie Croft

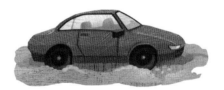

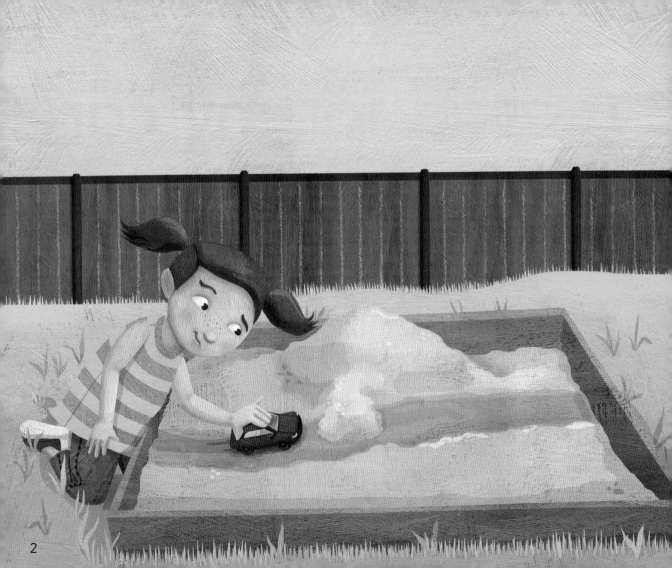

My car can not go
on the road.

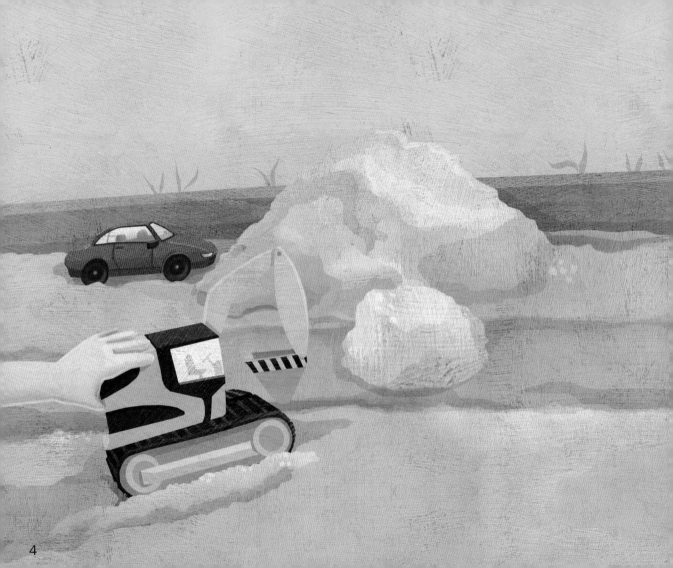

Here comes a digger.

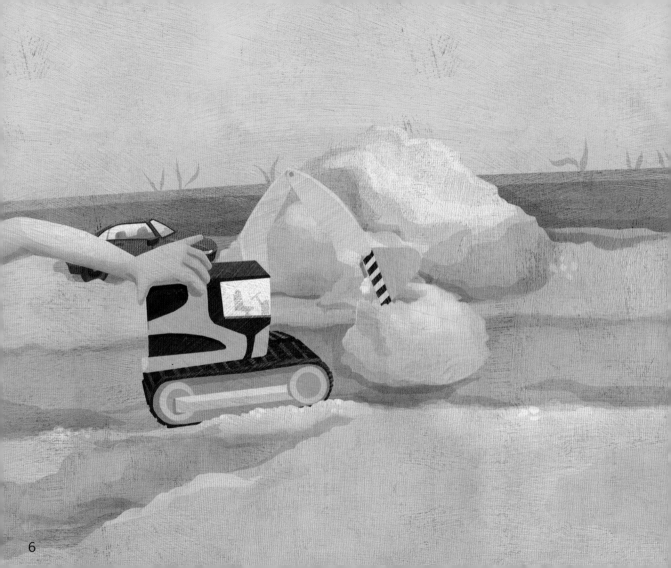

Look at the digger.

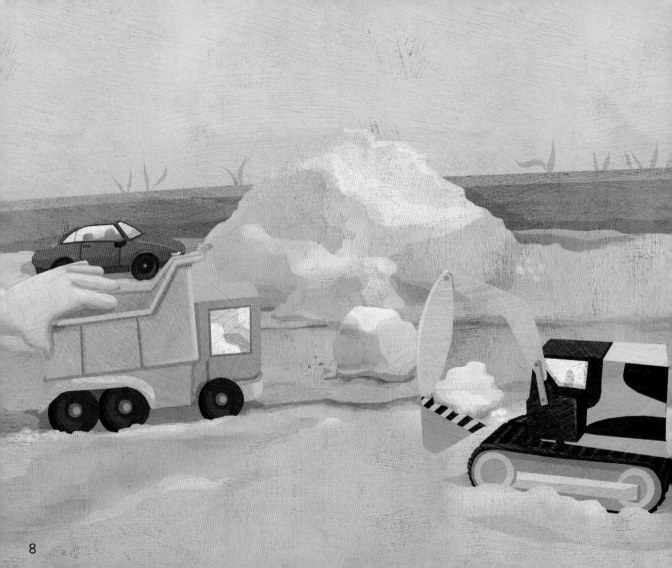

Here comes a truck.

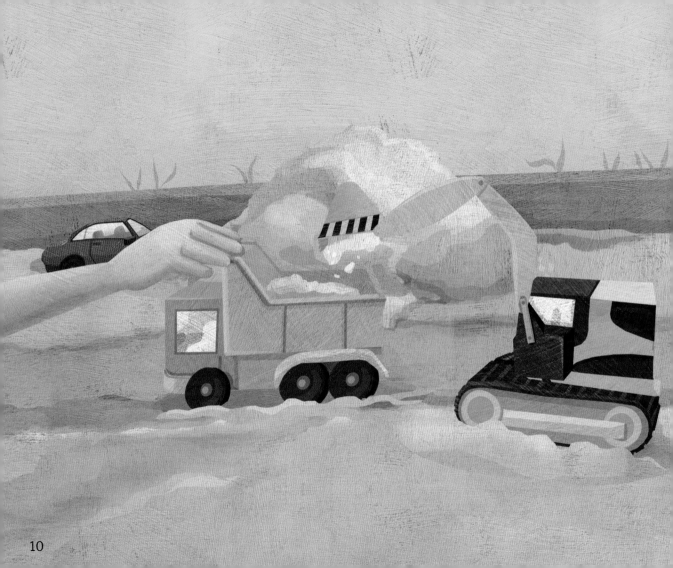

Look at the truck.

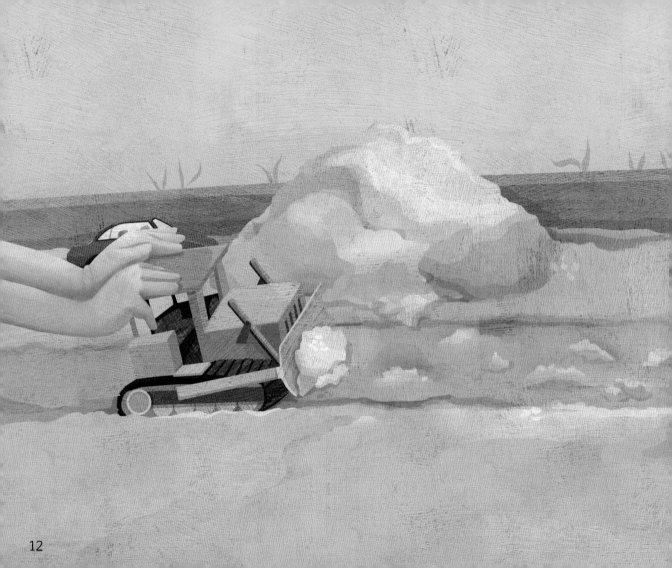

Here comes a bulldozer.

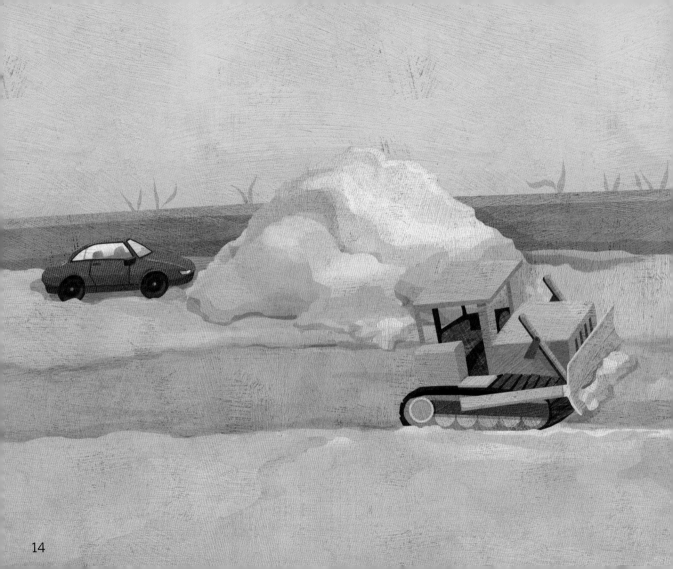

Look at the bulldozer.

My car can go
on the road.

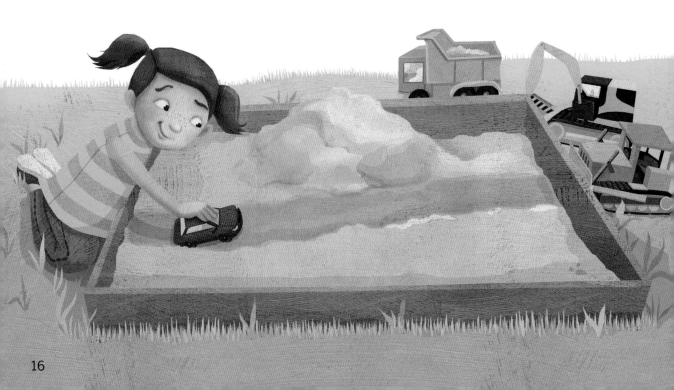